A GNOTE

Walk round to the back of this book. There you will find a picture of a GNU marked '10 o'clock Gnus'. Take a pencil and draw a clock on the body of the GNU with the small hand pointing to the 10 and the large hand pointing to the 12. And then it all happens.

The cover photograph of Spike Milligan as Benn Gunn
is from the Mermaid Theatre production of
Treasure Island 1967 Photograph by John Moss

Cover and typography by Lawrence Edwards

Published by Margaret & Jack Hobbs
Bridge Street, Walton-on-Thames, Surrey

Printed by Villiers Publications Ltd, Ingestre Road
London NW5

THE SINGING FOOT (A tale of a singing foot)

Woy Woy, Australia.
September 1967.

I have an Uncle. His name is Herbert Jam. He was 52. He worked
in a laundry. One Christmas Eve he was homeward bound on a
crowded bus when he heard what he thought was the sound of music
coming from inside his boot; indeed, what was to make him famous
had happened, his right foot had commenced to sing. Poor Mr. Jam
tried to control the volume of sound by tightening his boot lace; it
only succeeded in making the voice go from a deep baritone to a
strangled tenor. At the next stop Mr. Jam had to get off. He walked
home to the sound of his right foot singing 'God rest you merry
gentlemen', fortunately, Mr. Jam knew the words and mimed them
whenever people passed by. It was all very, very embarrassing. For
three days he stayed off work. His favourite T.V. programmes were
ruined by unexpected bursts of song from the foot, he did manage to
deaden it by watching with his foot in a bucket of sand, but, alas,
from this practice he contracted a rare foot rot normally only caught
by Arabs and camels. Worst was to come. The foot started singing at
night. At three in the morning he was awakened with
selections from 'The Gondoliers', 'Drake is going West' and 'A
Whiter Shade of Pale'. He tried Mrs. Helen Furg, a lady who was
known to have exorcised Poltergeists and Evil Spirits, she tied a
sprig of witchhazel round his ankle, intoned druidic prayers and burnt
all his socks in the bath, but it wasn't long before the strains of 'The
Desert Song' came lilting up his trouser leg again. On the recom-
mendation of his doctor he visited the great Harley Street right-foot
specialist, Sir Ralph Fees.
"Come in, sit down," said the great man, "Now, what appears to be
our trouble?"
"It's my right foot."
"Of course it is" said cheery Sir Ralph "and" he went on "what
appears to be the trouble with our right foot?"
"It sings."

Sir Ralph paused (but still went on charging) "You say your foot sings?"

"Yes, it's a light baritone" said wretched Jam.

Sir Ralph started to write. "I want you to go and see this Psychiatrist" he said — at which very moment Uncle Herbert's foot burst into song! "Just a minute" said Sir Ralph "I'll get my hat and come with you". The medical world and Harley Street were baffled. For the time he had to make do with a surgical sound-proof boot and a pair of wax ear-plugs. Occasionally, he would take off his boot to give the lads at the Pub a song, but, Mr. Jam was far from happy. Then came the beginning of the end, E.M.I. gave him a £500,000,000 contract for his foot to make records. A special group was formed, called 'The Grave', the billing was 'Mr. Jam with One Foot in the Grave'. He was the news sensation of the year! But, it became clear that it was the right foot that got the fame, not, Mr. Jam. E.M.I. opened a bank account for the right foot. While his poor left foot wore an old boot his right foot wore expensive purple alligator shoes from Carnaby Street which cost £50 a toe. At parties he was ceaselessly taking off his shoe to sign autographs! Mr. Jam was just an embarrassment to his right foot! One night in a fit of jealousy Mr. Jam shot his foot through the instep. It never sang again! Mr. Jam returned to the obscurity of his job in the laundry. He was 52, happy, only now he walked with a slight limp.

Rabbits they say
Are very scarce to-day -
my diagnosis?
~~~~ myxamatousis .

NON RABBIT
ELEPHANT.

Terence Newt
Wore a Giant boot
Jammed down over his head
And he ~~kept~~ it there
~~Well never at ease~~ {with his ears and claw}
Until the day he was dead.
But when his wife removed the Boot,
She discovered to her horror!
It was not the head of Terence Newt
But three other men. Tom Daft an apprentice
butcher, Cyril hunge a Mechanic and Arthur Woggs. Dent
~~th of no fixed abode~~.

Terence Newt
Wore a giant boot
Jammed down over his head
And he kept it there
With his ears and hair
Until the day he was dead.
But when his wife removed the boot,
She discovered to her horror!
It was not the head of Terence Newt
But three other men. Tom Daft an apprentice
butcher, Cyril Lunge a Mechanic, and
Arthur Woggs, Dentist.

Hopeless love

It is a hopeless time.
You are spring
And I —
Am Autumn.
Love can't close the gap.
And if it could — if it did —
One day you will be Autumn
And I Winter — and after that?

Midnight
Bournemouth
April 1967

A Boarding home
in Christchurch Rd

The Jet Plane —!
Brilliant — time saving
The new Icarus — and Tangled wings
And for me —
it just takes one from one unhappiness to another —
to another

The Young Soldiers

Why are they lying in some distant land
Why did they go, did they understand?
Young men they were
Young men they stay
But why did we send them away, away?

written during Korean War
March 30th 1955

Milleyammak

Get a Picture of a Gnw. Cut it out. place it over a news paper. Caption. The 10 o'clock Gnus.

Christmas Morning

A little girl called Silé Javotte
Said 'Look at the lovely presents I've got'.
A little girl in Biafra said
'Oh! What a lovely slice of bread.

Samson and Delilah

As he pushed the pillars apart
Samson was appalled
For just before the palace fell in
Delilah said 'He's bald!'.

Time Gentlemen

A-tick- A-tock.
Goes grandfather clock,
All through the night.
And every hour
With tremendous power
The clock would start to chime.

And may,
I say,
Its a noisy way,
For it,
to tell,
the Time.

A Nose

A World War II Nose

My nose, my nose lived dangerously
Its courage was no stunt!
And during the war in Germany
It was always out in front!

Yet when the battle was o'er
And we'd defeated the Hun
Suddenly, for no reason at all
My nose started to run.

These things called

The human face is something that
Hangs downwards from a thing called hat
And when the hat is raised, it's said
It shows a hairy thing called head.
Now I would rather cover face
And strike it full on with a mace.

Mermaid Theatre. 20 Dec. 1967

Brave New World

Twinkle Twinkle, little star
How I wonder what you are
Up above the sky so high
Like a almond in the sky

Twinkle Twinkle, little star
I've just found out what you are
A lump of rusting rocket case
A rubbish tip - in outer space.

14

Dear Reader!

Dublin
Nov. 1967

Human beings will become so used to being crushed together that when they are on their own, they will suffer withdrawal symptoms. "Doctor — I've got to get into a crowded train soon or I'll go mad". So, special N.H.S. assimilated rush hour trains will be run every other Sunday for patients. At 9 o'clock on that morning, thousands of victims will crowd platforms throughout England, where great electrically powered Crowd Compressors will crush hundreds of writhing humans into trains, until their eyes stand out under the strain, then, even more wretches are forced in by smearing them with vaseline and sliding them in sideways between legs of standing passengers. The doors close — any bits of clothing, ears or fingers are snipped off. To add to the sufferers' relief great clouds of stale cigarette smoke are pumped into the carriages. The patients start to cough, laugh and talk. They're feeling better already. But more happiness is on its way. The train reaches 80 m.p.h., at the next station the driver slams the brakes on shooting all the victims up to one end of the carriages. Immediately the doors open, and great compressed air tubes loaded with up to 100 passengers are fired into the empty spaces, this goes on until the rubber roofs of the carriages give upwards, and the lumps you see are yet a second layer of grateful patients. Off goes the train, and one sees the relief on the travellers' faces. Who wants LSD when you can get this? Ah! you say, the train can't possibly take any more. Wrong! At the next stop the train is sprayed with a powerful adhesive glue, and fresh passengers stuck to the outside, and so, crushed to pulp, pop-eyed and coughing blood, the train carries out its work of mercy. Those who are worried about their children's future in the 20th century need not fear. We are prepared.

Phillip le Barr
Was knocked down by a car
On the road to Mandalay
He was knocked down again
By a dust cart in Spain
And again, in Zanzibar
So,
He travelled at night
In the pale moon-light
Away from the traffic's growl
But terrible luck
He was hit by a duck
Driven by — an owl.

Mr. Timothy Pringle
Lived on his own
As he was single.
Returning from work
In the evening gloom
He found an elephant
In his room.
It had a label
Round its neck
"My name is Doris
Eileen Beck".
Even if the name was Jim
It didn't really help poor Tim.
Is that elephant a her or he?
Asked Mr. Screws (the landlady)
Tim said "It's a female elephant, why?"
"No women in rooms" was the stern reply.

Mr Timothy Pringle
Lived on his own
As he was single.
Returing from work
In the evening gloom
He found an Elephant
In his room
It had a $label)
Round its neck
"My name is Doris
Eileen Beck".
Even if the name Jim
It didn't really help poor Tim.
Is that Elephant a her or he?
Asked Mr Screws [his landlady]
Tim said Its a female elephant why?
"No women in rooms" was the stern reply

VALUES '67

Pass by Citizen:
   don't look left or right,
keep those drip dry eyes straight ahead.
A tree? Chop it down.
     they're a danger to lightning
Pansies, calling for water?
     Let 'em die — the queer bastards!
Seek comfort in the scarlet plastic
      labour saving rose
Fresh with the fragrance of Daz.
Sunday. Pray citizen:
   pray that no rain will fall
     on your newly polished
       four wheeled
        God.

Envoi. Beauty is in the eye of the beholder. Get it out — with Optrex.

On a train to Liverpool, Easter Monday 1967.

Little tiny puppy dog
Sleeping soundly as a log
Better wake him for his dinner
Or else he'll start to sleep much thinner.

22

3rd of Sliptimber
The Olleth of Arg

Dear Reader,
    At last I've completed my first reliable Leaping Stone. This Stone
is a simple method of forcing oneself to leap and as a result become
quite an expert, the best places to place these stones are (I) Halfway
up the stairs — in the Centre of the Bathroom door — or in the
middle of the front garden gate. The stone — roughly the shape of
an old Grave stone, should be wide enough to block a passage
around it, and 3 ft. 2 in. high. Once a client has shown interest in
leaping stones several demonstration stones should be cemented
into his house — one in every door in fact, a Leapo-meter is attached
to the ankle of every member of the family, which records the number
of leaps per person, per day, per-haps. Those who show disinterest
can have a small explosive charge fixed to the groin, which
detonates should the person try climbing round these stones, this
will cause many a smoke blackened crutch, but with our new spray-
on 'Crutcho' — a few squirts leave the groins gleaming white and
free of foul-pest. Think of the enervating joys of the Leaping stones!
Sunday morn — and the whole household rings with shouts of Hoi
Hup! Ho la! Grannies — uncles — Mothers — cripples — all leaping
merrily from one room to another — ah, there's true happiness. We
have high hopes that more progressive young politicians with an eye
to eliminating senile M.P.s, intend to have a 'Great Westminster
Leaping Stone' that will be placed dead centre of the Great entrance
doors on the opening day of Parliament — those failing will of course

be debarred — though they can claim 'A brethren assisted leap' — this means that two decrepit M.P.s of the same party, can try and assist the failed member over the leaping stone by applying hot pokers to the seat, thus the smell of scorched seats, burning hairs and screams, can bring a touch of colour to an otherwise dull occasion. I don't know when I will post this letter, I might deliver it tomorrow by hand, ankle, foot and clenched elbow.

As ever,
Spike.

It's in
here
somewhere

An Ear passed me
    the other day
And silently
    went on its way

I wonder who
    that ear can be
And has it ever
    heard of me.

Oh the Wiggley - Woggley men
They don't get up till ten
They run about
Then give shout
And go back to bed again!

Oh the Wiggley-Woggley men
They don't get up till ten
They run about
Then give a shout
And back to bed again!

28

Norrington Blitt
Ate aught but grit
Ate aught but grit and mussels
But when he got there
The cupboard was bare
Save a sack of sprouts —
From Brussels, or was it Oldham?
No — a tree fell on him.
Or was —

Manic Depression

St. Lukes Wing
Woodside Hospital
Psychiatric Wing   1953 -

The pain is too much
A thousand grim winters
　grow in my head.
In my ears
　the sound of the
　　coming dead
All seasons, all same
　all living
　all pain
No opiate to lock still
　my senses.
Only left, the body locked tenser.

December 1960.

Dec. 1960

Manic Depression

The pain is too much
A thousand grim winters
    grow in my head.

In my ears
        the sound of the
            coming dead

All seasons, all same
        all living
        all pain

No opiate to lock still
            my senses.

Only left, the body locked tenses.

31

Freedom

A bird in flight,
  her wings spread wide
Is the soul of man
    with bonds untied
Beyond the plough
    the spade, the God
A bird flies in
    the face of God,

Yet I with reason
    bright as day
Forever tread
    the earthbound clay.

PARIS PAREE

Written in Paris when
I went last time.

Paris! Paree! What pictures of gaiety those two cities conjour up,
down, and sideways, Paris, city of Napoleon, the Revolution, the Mob,
the blood, the head rolling. Alas, those happy days are gone, yet,
Paris, the Queen of cities calls us all. Last week it called me, 'Cooee!'
it said and I responded. Travel allowance being only £50, I saved by
taking sandwiches and a Thermos of Tomato Sauce. I saved further
on the air fare by travelling second class non-return tourist night
flight, all you had to do was sign a Secret Enoch Powell form saying
you were an undesirable coloured alien with incurable bed-wetting. At
the airport, there was the carefully disguised panic rush to get the
back seats in the plane. On take-off I fastened my safety belt, read
'How to inflate Life Belt', swallowed a boiled sweet, made the sign
of the cross and read the Times. One hour later coming in to Orly I
fastened my copy of the Times, made the sign of the seat belt,
swallowed by boiled life belt and inflated myself for landing. Through
to Customs and out! At the airport my taxi drew up in a cloud of
Garlic, and the driver leapt out and gesticulated in a corner. Arriving
at the Hotel, the porter raised his hat and lowered his trousers. Real
French hospitality! The Hotel had been built in 1803 — in 1804 they
added a west wing and in 1819 it flew away. Next morning I was up
at the crack of noon shouting "Apres moi le deluge" and whistling
Toulouse Lautrec, I hurriedly swallowed a breakfast of porridge and
frogs and a steaming bidet of coffee. I next joined a crowd of

impoverished British tourists on the 30 centimes all-in English punishment Tour. A great herd of us assembled at the Place du Concord, from there we were force-marched to the Notre Dame, beaten with sticks and made to climb the great Bell Tower. Sheer physical agony! On the way up we passed many who had perished in the attempt and never made it. Fancy! 600 steps! No wonder Quasi Modo had a hump on his back when he got to the top! From the top I took several lovely photos of the Eiffel Tower. At Midday, we were led to a Cafe 'Le Gogo Plastique', the establishment bore the indelible stamp of the British tourists —

Menu

'Escargots and mash . . .'
'Bisque d'Homard, bread and butter'
'Pate de Fois Gras and Chips'
'Lobster Thermidor, 2 Veg., Boiled Pots. etc.'
'Crepe Suzette Flambe and Custard'

The lady next to me had Frogs' legs, her friend's weren't much better. It's all that walking, I suppose. I was served by a waiter who made it perfectly clear he held me personally responsible for a) The loss of Algeria b) Waterloo c) Edith Piaff. Just so they didn't think I was an oaf, I ordered the whole meal in French — I was brought a hip-bath, a silk tie, a coloured pencil and a small clockwork Virgin Mary that whistled Ave Maria every hour, made in Hong Kong. I spent the rest of the afternoon sketching the beautiful Eiffel Tower. There's always something to do in Paris! Carefully following my Baedecker's Paris I walked up the hill to the Cemetery of Pierre Lachaze, I saw the very spot where Moulin Rouge lay buried, and above me gleaming white was the Sacred Cur, now used as a church. I had been walking some three hours and as a quick calculation showed me that I was exactly six miles from the lovely Eiffel Tower, I took a taxi back to the Pension; to my horror he asked for 13 francs, I was about to have a show down with him, but, rather than ruin the evening, I paid him. It ruined the evening. I freshened up in my room, taking a shower and a foot-bath in a very low basin with a rather dangerous water jet that took me completely by surprise. The evening would be dedicated to Art, I always wanted to see the French Impressionists so I booked for the Folie Bergere where a man was doing imitations of Maurice Chevalier, Josephine Baker, and many others. What a show! Women uncovered from the waist up, and yet there was a cover charge! Watching women with naked bosoms is unsettling, but eventually they grow on you. If they grew on me I'd go to the pictures alone. The Grand Finale was called 'Salute les Anglais', the band played a Pop version of God Save the Queen while a French queer wearing a Prince Philip mask juggled with three Plastic Busts of the heir presumptive. It was good to see that we were still a country to be respected. If only we had their Eiffel Tower there'd be no stopping us.

29

Painted in 1866

(canvas 11″ ×

Blot on the Landscape

36

George Melley
Had such a fat Belly
He couldn't get near the Telly
So he had to go
And listen to the Radio.

All the ravel-avel tumble-umblings — all the high sorrows —
All going all giving all taking all doing. Which, what
When where how — worse still. Who? Who's next? —
I know — it's me — it's always me; time for it now sir —
Now son — now — now — NOW it's time for it. Yes.
Now the drop down starts — sitting, standing, kneeling
Lying — the drop starts — down down — it's always down —
Some time down stops — but it only stops at down — then
Off it goes again — down, down, down, into the unanswerable.

Over Elba — September, 1967.
Drunk

Skeleton of Prehistoric Car

Bronte cycle

Said the mother Tern
   to her baby Tern
Would you like a brother?
Said baby Tern
   to mother Tern
Yes
One good Tern deserves another.

Sent to Chiselhurst & Sidcup College.

I see those two have fallen
out with each other.

9 Orme Court,
Bayswater,
W.2.
13 June, 1963.
Sir,

     Whereas the Bishop of Southwark is to be complimented on his speech (Times, 13 June '63) when he speaks of "corruption in high places", what he should have said was "curruption in all places". To point the finger of indictment at one or two persons, is almost laughable when one considers the extent of moral corruption in this country as a whole, and this corruption feeds on the licence it is allowed by the feeble Church and Parliamentary laws, which almost condone it. Pornography, which is the greatest inciter of immorality, is not only rife, but actually bestowed, in some spheres, as 'art', by the intellectuals, which is quickly exploited by all commercial enter-prises. Films of rape, murder, sex, debasement, are now 'la mode', to criticise them is to be 'old hat'. The X certificate is box-office bonanza. Even innocent comedies have publicity that is aimed at sex. As a parent, I find it increasingly difficult to take my children to see a suitable film. Bookstalls in all our major cities groan under the weight of pornographic 'literature', Mens 'clubs' doing nothing but strip-shows, drinking clubs show films that are laughingly called 'Naked but free' etc., etc. Photographic pornography, using safe Box numbers, is a million pound trade. In the light of this I fear Dr. Stockwood's address will have little or no effect at all, yet, it is in religious laxity that the seeds of immorality grow, and, at this critical stage in history, never has the Christian church been so inactive and indifferent to the massive danger to Christianity. Take China as an example, the Christians were in China 500 years before Communism. Today in China, Christianity hardly exists, why? Parrot-indoctrination; give the native a vest, a crucifix, one chorus of 'Onward Christian

Soldiers', and he's ticked off as being a Christian, and still Christians are churned out as tho' from a mould, size is no substitute for quality. I myself was baptised a Catholic, and I still don't know what it is all about, nobody ever bothered to teach me. Year after year I listen for a message of enlightenment from the pulpit, but no, the Gospels, the Epistles, are repeated ad nauseum, but of contemporary guidance there is nothing. Going round saying "And the Lord said unto Moses" won't get us anywhere, Jesus didn't talk about throwing the money lenders out of the Temple, he did it, then talked. If we are to stop the moral rot, we must act, we must indict, we must mention the offenders by name and not hide for fear of libel, the truth is all that matters, right now this country is not geared to accept it. Consider, that England, France, Italy, West Germany and America are where pornography abounds, and these are the countries dedicated to preserve Christianity from the Godless Russia who has no pornography.

Spike Milligan

A little poem for Sean

There was a young boy called Sean
Who sat on the edge of a lawn
His knees went crack!
He fell on his back
And regretted the day he was born.

I sent my legs out for a walk
To keep them strong and fit
They would not go without me
So I've made the b . . . . . s sit.

THINK OF THE MONEY YOU'LL SAVE IN TRANSPORT.

47

Cautionary Letter

Green Bonk

Dear reader, the worst has happened. Brown Bonk has struck in the Quantocks. Worse still, attacks of Green Bonk have been reported coming from the Urals; an Armenian fruit shepherd was driving a herd of Apple trees to water when the Brown Bonk laid him low. The first case of our own Brown Bonk was at Catford Labour Exchange. Mr. Ted Naffs was being given his certificate for 21 years of devoted unemployment, when, yes! Brown Bonk! Smoke started to issue from Mr. Naffs' mouth, a scream of agony showed his teeth to be molten white. He was rushed to a blacksmith who removed his ring of confidence. Toothless with Brown Bonk, Mr. Naffs was given a pair of N.H.S. electric teeth, for high speed eating, a boon to the aged and infirm. Leave the food and teeth by your bed at night and they do your eating while you sleep. Alas, Mr. Naffs' house, was all Gas. An application had to be made for a set of North Sea High Speed Gas-operated Teeth. While he was waiting for delivery Mr. Naffs stupidly plugged into the great overhead cables of the National Electric grid which ran over his cottage. As he switched on 100,000,000 volts shot into his 240 volt teeth, a brilliant flash of magnesium, and his dentures started to chew at round about the speed of light, Mr. Naffs' head became a white blurr as his teeth ate the porridge — the plate — knife — fork — spoon — table mat — the table — the chairs — the dog — the cat — two budgies — a Welsh dresser, he was half way through a brick wall when the annual power failure saved him. Beware all of you, Brown Bonk is with us, at the first sign of smouldering teeth. . . . . Write to the fire brigade.

I had a Dongee
Who would not speak
He wouldnt hop
He wouldnt creep
He wouldnt walk
He wouldnt leap
He wouldnt wake
He wouldnt sleep
He wouldnt shout
He wouldnt squeak
He wouldnt look
He wouldnt peep
He wouldnt wag
  his Dongee tail.
I think this Dongees
    going to fail.

If Robert Graves
   misbehaves
It's the Torjca
   Majorca

The sayings of Mrs. Doris Reach
of 23 The Irons, Cleethorpes, Herts.

1. Ups a Daisy
2. Save the string.
3. There's some in the tin on the Mantlepiece.
4. They should never let them in the country.
5. Ups a Daisy
6. I had an Aunt who was like that.
7. Mine's Brown.
8. Just a small one then.
9. Ups a Daisy.
10. It comes off with Turps.
11. He knows every word you say.
12. Ups a Daisy.
13. What about a nice. . . . .
14. Ups a Daisy.

Editor. Rag Mag., Gloucester College of Education.

You say your mag. is in aid of mental health! Dear Lad, there's no such thing, if there was anybody in position of power with any semblance of mental health do you think the world would be in this bloody mess? Young minds at risk is different. Anybody with a young mind is taking a risk — young means fresh — unsullied, ready to be gobbled up in an adult world bringing the young into visionless world of adults, like all our leaders. Their world is dead — dead — dead, and my God, that's why it stinks! They look at youth in horror — and say 'They are having a revolution', but what do they want? I say they don't know what they want, but they know what they don't want, and that is, the repetition of the past mistakes, towards which the adult old order is still heading. War — armistice — building up to pre-war standards — capitalism — labour — crisis — war and so on. I digress.

Mental Health. I have had five nervous breakdowns — and all the medics gave me was medicine — tablets — but no love or any attempt at involvement, in this respect I might as well have been a fish in a bowl. The mentally ill need LOVE, UNDERSTANDING — TOLERANCE, as yet unobtainable on the N.H.S. or the private world of psychiatry, but tablets, yes, and a bill for £5 5. 0. a visit — if they know who you are it's £10 10. 0. a visit — the increased fee has an immediate depressing effect — so you come out worse than you went in.

As yet, I have not been cured, patched up via chemicals, yes. Letter unfinished, but I've run out of time — sorry!

Regards,
Spike

Once there was a girl
Who grew roses in my head
Made a paradise of bed
Yet not a word was said.

My Street

ass by
ll the blinds
lothing happened here to-day

'ouse the light
    lock the door.

       nothings happened.

Valk the street
    turn the corner
       nothing there. forever more
           of

What was it
so quick.
So Unthought
Yet - Alright
It was'nt me
It was'nt you
Yet it was —
Before "
After "
During
We were looking
for the
answer to
one plus one

What was it -
So quick
So Unthought
Yet - all right?
It wasn't me
or you -
then - it was
Before -
After
During - supply the same
We're just at the own show
to the sea
let :

Rennie Scotts Club

What was it?
So quick
So unthought
Yet — Alright
It wasn't me
It wasn't you
Yet it was —
Before
  After
    During.

We were looking for the
answer to one plus one.

Ronnie Scotts Club.

S. Milligan

"No, no, try ASPIRIN."

Dear Lads,

I am so overwhelmed with work at the moment, and by this, I don't mean the sheer monetary kind; I also try and have an interest in humanity.

Anyhow, I just haven't got time for an article. However! I would like to state that I have been aware of the coming dissent among students for the last ten years against a world, which has become archaic in ideas, and the extension of those ideas.

The normal channels left open to citizens to complain are crammed to the brink, and normally no individual citizen can get anything changed under the present system, unless he is willing to spend £10,000 and go to litigation, that, or set fire to himself outside No. 10 Downing Street, which would, in turn, only result in a bucket of water from the Prime Minister.

Whereas, students are not at all clear as to what they want, they certainly know what they don't want.

The old world and its standard formula of democracy are spent forces, who can only go on repeating past mistakes on the same democratic basis, among these we have over-population, starvation, war, political unrest, and archaic laws which themselves are evil. One only has to investigate the modern divorce law to discover to what disgusting levels human beings are reduced, to obtain a divorce.

Religion has become unchristian, the Christ that lived would certainly look extremely embarrassed and out of place in the Vatican. Christian morals have changed to such an extent that people are now on the verge of accepting debasement as some form of art. Jesus chose a donkey. Top clergy use Austin Princesses!

I myself am not a prude, but I am finding it difficult to find a film, a book, or a magazine that does not use the sex act as the basis of world art form.

All this is being seen very clearly by student bodies around the world, and through the extraordinary combustion exploding at the same time.

Unfortunately, the old guard are so firmly entrenched and the system so protected by armed forces, police and lackies, that only civil war can bring about a change.

Modern student thinking is violently opposed to the use of arms (or at least it should be), but student bodies must keep up the pressure for the rest of their lives to try and influence their wives, and children and children's children into thinking of a new method for man to live on this earth. Governments can start by solving the most important problem in the world, over-population, which in itself leads to the lowering of all man's standards.

I haven't time to say much more, but let us say that the old world has got to change, and by the old world I also mean these idiots who want to get to the moon, when man hasn't really got to the earth.

Sincerely,
Spike Milligan

P.S. I keep fighting.

Its little God,

When my daddys in the bath
I knock upon the door
'Whos dat' he says
But I don't say and then?
.I knock some more,
'Whos dad' hes says' Whos dat aga
And he must think its odd
,For when at last I answer him
'Its me' I say "Its God!"

He swung to and fro
Then   3 and fro
        4 and fro
        5 and fro
And finally 6 and fro.

SUN HELMET

A pleasant three degrees below zero wind was blowing. The early morning Londoners shivered through the bitingly cold rush hour. Among them was a bowler-hatted Mr. Oliver Thrigg. The first snow of summer was starting to fall as he joined his 'AA members only' bus cue. Glancing to a bus que opposite (it was a different que to his cue, as the spelling proves), and what he saw shook him to his foundation garment. There, in the que opposite, was a man wearing a sun helmet, eccentricity yes, but this fellow didn't have a stamp of a genuine eccentric, no, fellow looked far too normal! Curiosity got the upper hand, crossing the road he killed a cat. Once across he joined the que and left his on the other side. The man in the sun-helmeted man caught a 31A bus, Mr. Thrigg signalled a passing 49A. "Follow that bus" he told the driver. "Anywhere but Cuba" said the driver. At Victoria Station the sun-helmeted man booked to Southampton, as did Mr. Thrigg, who kept him under surveyaliance until they reached Southampton, where by now the snow was 3 foot deep, which explained the absence of dwarfs in the street. The man continued to wear his sun helmet. "Why, Why, Why" said Thrigg whose curiosity had killed another nine cats, making a grand total of one. "I must follow this man etc." The man booked aboard the Onion Castle and was handed £10 and an oar (Assisted Passage they call it). The ship headed south, and, so did Mr. Thrigg and his enigma, which he used for colonic irrigation. During the whole trip the man appeared at all times in a sun helmet. Several or eightal times he was almost tempted to ask the man his secret. But no, as Thrigg was travelling steerage and the man 1st Class, plus the fact it was a special Non-fraternising Apartheid Cruise, no contact was possible. On the 12th of Iptomber the ship docked at Cape Town. Even though Thrigg got through Customs and Bribes at speed, he just missed the Sun Helmet as he drove off in a taxi. Thrigg flagged down an old cripple Negro driver "Follow that Sun Helmet" he said jumping on the nigger's back. (The change from Negro to Nigger denotes change from UK to SA soil.) Several times Thrigg let the nigger stand in his bucket of portable UK soil so he could be called Negro. To cut the story short, Mr. Thrigg used scissors and cornered the man in the middle of the Sahara. The heat was intolerable as Thrigg walked up and said "Why are you wearing that sun helmet?" "Because" said the man, pointing at a 113° thermometer in the shade "The sun man! This protects the head." "I see" said Mr. Thrigg. "Well I better be off, I'm late for work." As he departed for the caravan que, the man in the sun helmet spotted him. "Good God, a man wearing a bowler hat! A bowler hat? Here, in the Sahara? I must find out why," he thought as he joined the caravan cue behind Mr. Thrigg.

Titikaka

The magic green lake
that fell from the sky,
quenched a burning mountain's throat
and sent a fire king
into untimeable slumber.

On a plane over Mexico. Sept. 1968.

Morning

Chamfers of White
        Light
Shaft from the cheap 20th Century glass
Flared on my bed
        Red
Blanket barks its reflection to the ear in
                my eye
And so it
        bit
By bit pulls together the strings of morning.

January 4 at 'Old Place'

Lashing - tree

At the third stroke
it will be 3.29

70

A bottle of Graves
             or Graves
I ordered in half
             or halves

The 12th June
is very soon
for there is a party on that Day
and most likly I be going away

Silke..
June 6

The 18th June
Is very soon
For there is a party
   on that day
And most likely I be
   going away.

Silé.   June 1967

How teeny teeny wee
Is the teeny little flea.
But last night in my hotel
He made me scratch like merry hell!

THE TALE OF FRANCIS PAW by Margaret and Jack Hobbs

There was a cat called Francis Paw
Who lived behind the kitchen door
He was old and brown
And tumbledown
But his fur was long and silky
He liked an egg for breakfast
And some tea if it was milky.

He often sat in an old silk hat
And talked to me of this and that
He liked a joke
And his voice would croak
As he told me of his youth.

He used to croon
To the harvest moon
And sing a roundelay
Of his Uncle Fred
Who is long since dead
Who went to Botany Bay.

He went aboard a whaling boat
Which foundered in a gale
With feline craft
He clung to a raft
With the end of his scraggy tail.

At last he reached an island fair
And struggled to the shore
Where under a tree
Stood Sam Macgee
Staring at Frederick Paw.

'Yo Ho' he cried
'The cook has died
'What can we have to eat?'
'You look a tasty morsel, lad,
'Except for your smelly feet.'

Fred's ears went flat
'I'll catch a rat'
He said in trembling tones
There isn't very much of me
I'm only skin and bones.

'I would' said Sam
'Prefer a ham'
But I'll give you an hour
To catch a rat that's big and fat
And cook it rolled in flour.

Fred caught a rat
And that was that
And rescue soon was nigh
In the shape of a Chinese sailor
By the name of Wun Flung Hi.

Wun Flung Hi
Had a drooping eye
And a most unsavoury crew
They hit poor Fred
And Sam on the head
And put 'em in Hold No. 2.

They sat in the hold
Through the long dark night
Wondering what to do
When the hatch was raised
And down there gazed
The face of Fu Manchu.

Fu Manchu was a prisoner too
For a ransom so they say
But he'd opened the lock
With a piece of a clock
And planned a getaway.

Fred and Sam and Fu Manchu
Took a boat and sailed away.
And when the dawn
Of the day was born
They landed at Botany Bay.

What happened then
I chose to ask
Of my friend, young Francis Paw
That's another tale
He yawned and fell
Asleep by the kitchen door.